MAD
SAD & GLAD

1st printing . . . . December 1970
Printed in the U. S. A.

Editor's note . . .

A year ago I was asked to select poems I admired and liked from hundreds of winners in Scholastic Magazines' "Creative Writing Awards" program. This book is the result—an anthology of 101 award-winning poems from 1966 through 1970.

In gratitude for an exciting year, I dedicate MAD SAD & GLAD to the young writers whose poems appear in the book. Their ideas, their music, and their language are good for today, and promise even better things for tomorrow.

To the hundreds of other award-winners whose poems were not chosen for the book, I also owe thanks. They made the job of choosing difficult, but that was part of the fun.

To Claudia Johnson, Tim Conners, and Steven Dunning, high school students of Ann Arbor, Michigan, this key acknowledgment: Your judgments of the hundreds of poems you read made my final decisions possible, but not easy.

Stephen Dunning
Ann Arbor, Michigan
May 23, 1970

SECTION ONE

MOM LET TOMMY BABYSIT
(She was only going next door.)

Lights-out spookiness —
We whispered and giggly laughed,
jumped bed to bed,
funny-faced Kelly made watermelon mouths
at the moon.
All silly and laughy
we romped,
making shadow pictures
on a moon-eerie wall,
losing giggles in our hands.
When a noise
froze us —
scared us quiet —
So closely we listened
to stair creaks and
door rattles —
Peered each other across the room,
scaredy, bug-eyed Kelly with the watermelon mouth.
Then dared to move.
Dark grew darker and crept around us.
Slow, tired seconds,
then sleepy minutes
passed.

Joseph Graham
St. Edward High School
Cleveland, Ohio
1969

MIKE CARREL ALWAYS WORE

his pants almost to his neck
and one time virgil phillips sucked
all the ink out of a pen
into his mouth
mrs beavers wouldn't let me
carve in wax in art
cause i told her i could do it real good
i was fibbing at the time
but she said "if you already know how,
we'll let you work in clay"
boy did i ever hate clay
and phil mcdaniels fell down at recess
and cut his bottom
but he was embarrassed to have mrs rogers
look at it or fix it but he was really bleeding
so she let a 6th grader fix it
he was red all day and i don't mean his bottom
either
miss crawford told us every day how
smart she was and
how her oboe would fit in her underarm
but we all liked singing better
mrs harod who really rode a wagon in the
land run
would drink cough syrup right out of the bottle
and by last period
she would sure act silly
once she asked us to learn limericks
for the next day
and ole virgil phillips
learned the dirtiest one
i'd ever heard and
mrs harod got choked and nearly
passed on right then
mean old miss habor hit bucky one time

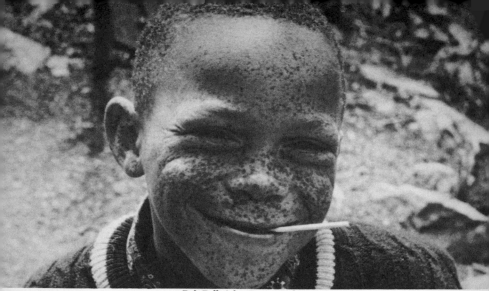

Bob Fulbright, Forest Park High School, Beaumont, Tex.

so hard he fell outa his chair
and it was scotty who was talking
mike morris told dirty jokes at recess
ole mike was really popular
i'd laugh and laugh
but i didn't really understand
i wanted to ask somebody but i was afraid
one time there was this word on the sidewalk
and bucky pretended he didn't know it
so i sounded it out
and it was nasty
and everybody laughed
but when mrs matheson
would read to us
about holland
i'd think about holland and
be real happy
and 4th grade sure went fast

Kevin Bales
Ponca City Senior High School
Ponca City, Oklahoma
1970

BOY WITH A GUN

I see him from the window, crouching low,
With gun upraised, and eyes so innocent
And anxious, peering at his prey.

I could have him leave — for he's hunting
In my yard — but there are other birds
And places. And those eyes — I've seen
Him smooth the ruffled feathers
Of a fresh-killed robin — the lust
Is not yet there.

> He wants to see the bird,
> To hold it; he knows no other way.

But I shall teach him:
> Tomorrow I will smell the sparkling dew,
> And maybe he will, too.

Doyle McKey
Edna High School
Edna, Texas
1967

RAINY-DAY CHILD

Into the wind one
Autumn-day-child in
hysterical yellow rain slicker
chases drowning leaf
to its gutter grave;
his laughter, riotous bubbles
slashing the greyness
with the brilliance
        of child-joy.

Beth Lacey
Moorestown Senior High School
Moorestown, New Jersey
1967

Judi Bronson, Norwood (N. Y.)-Norfolk Central High School

NOEL

He had disappeared one december night
        down the street
        to buy a christmas tree
A great tall green one he said
            and he showed how big with his hands
And all the children shouted
            and planned popcorn and cranberry
                strings
            And then he just went out and
never came home
            They went out with lanterns
    of course and later they cried
            But the children went next door and
            stole the neighbors' tree and
put a naked angel
            on the top

David Walker
Durham High School
Durham, North Carolina
1967

13

YELLOW CUP AND PLASTIC SPOON

Yellow cup and plastic spoon
rattle like summer in Michael's hand.
Day move in Michael's eyes.
Grass, she say things.
Men run like puppies, see?
Chasing tails, hey.
Michael is thinking in twos.
feeling air twice warm.
"What say you Michael boy?
Warm enough for you lad?"
Michael rattles spoon in cup.
Can't say can't say

Can't do nothing but breathe wind and cherries,
touch grass that weep
to make her laugh.
Michael pull down sky to see the blue,
wait with summer
like sand in a bucket
then let go
of grass and sky
and rattle cup
no more
no more

Larry Libby
North Eugene High School
Eugene, Orgeon
1969

Gregg Smith, Onalaska (Wisc.) High School

SECTION TWO

IN THE MORNING FEELING POEM
(for Debbie Smith)

now sometimes, no always
when i awaken
and tramp into the bathroom
brush my teeth,
and that tired feeling, like
no head belongs on my shoulders, and
then when i finally find my head thinking that
i didn't do my homework and so what
and then the sun shines through the window so
scrambled eggs which i eat
all this preparing for
school and all
how wonderful
to love you so much

Steve Light
Robert A. Milliken High School
Long Beach, California
1969

Carol Erickson, Reseda (Calif.) High School

Bruce Berman, Palm Springs (Calif.) High School

CHANT AT SUNDOWN

breath of incense
legs of stone
eyes of topaz
every bone
of him is mine

I take my time.

Patience Merriman
Cardinal O'Hara High School
Springfield, Pennsylvania
1969

19

UNION

If I marry
   there will be no frosting-sick cake,
   no curl-lettered namecards,
   no long-veil organ march,
   no red wet-eyed happiness,
   no silver-heavy gift tables,
   no sticky sweet mint tray,
   no life-watching minister,
   and no angel voices.
But the sun will leap
   as we run wild
      to windsung poems . . .
And the moon will pearl
   as we hum home,
        remembering.

Meg Fisher
Urbana High School
Urbana, Illinois
1967

FOR LADY

you were right.   Lady, and
wednesday   wore deep red, and sat
               in the corner of his universe.
not like: friday of the cool eyes, who did not believe in
death or romance, who was
content to watch the green hourglass ooze lovelessness.
   And not like
      you and i, lady (you & i who are of the eager
        flesh) —
     we were apart, with our wordless speech
             (sitting in the Soul's Airport as we did)

And deep in the uncertainty of early morning (sweet
   blues) we
drank our deep-red wednesday wine: "That
           goeth down sweetly, causing
           the lips of those that are asleep
                   to speak"
Transforming the shadows of my trees,
evolving spring from the death of winter's brain —
    And who are they? what do they will? ah,
      wednesday, friday,
the song of april . . .

             O Lady, you were right.
(an unrehearsed love) and the strange trees
were right: singing of the eager flesh.
(lady and i in the airport,
    Praying, and watching the great planes
                   come in.)

Eric A. Smith
East High
Salt Lake City, Utah
1967

LONG DISTANCE BIRTHDAY

The sixteenth candle gives out,
splatters wax across the good tablecloth;
Alice,
her pigtails in the inkwell,
still sings to the icing.
Her party hat wrinkled, trim frayed,
elastic snapped,
she has been rerouted through the hourglass
screaming at some vanishing whiteness.

Last year
you came to me in printed wrappings
with curled ribbons and rules book.
Today I clutched the curled cord,
cut your heart from my calendar,
poked it in the ballot box
and deliberated:
the clock changed hands, the
seventeenth candle spurted to life
and the telephone slid from my fingers
back to its cradle.

Denise Zelany
Finney High School
Detroit, Michigan
1969

Thomas Frei, North Haven (Conn.) High School

A DAYSONG

i am the open-armed sky

rolling over on my blue tummy
thinking in short white puffs

and my love is a single seagull
circling my thoughts always,
flashing his silver wings
at the afternoon,

skywriting his praise
on my blue-gray knees

and i love him because

the bony moon
and all the polished nightstars
in my hair

have no heartbeat
and can sing me no songs.

Patience Merriman
Cardinal O'Hara High School
Springfield, Pennsylvania
1969

Gregory Lefko, Palo Verde High School, Tucson, Ariz.

IRRESPONSE

Promises of
Undying love
Have melted
Into
So many bowls
Of vegetable soup
Mixed with
Emotions unspent
Now pent
Up
In a greasy fog
Which steams the glass
On bedroom windows.

Lola Sierra
Alverno Heights Academy
Sierra Madre, California
1969

EPILOGUE

Now it is over.   It wasn't very long
And I can say good-bye without regrets
(Or at least few) and   softly
Wave away your face.   But I can wish
And truly do, my dear
That you had known me in
The summer months.

In days of dust and
Late long shadows
I am golden-bright   scratched   faded
Softly tattered   and the silent
Crease-lines of confusion
Disappear
From in between eyes   hands   feet   turning
Into laughing   cheerful   sunburnt
Freckled brown
And gleaming-damp
Smooth flesh
(At least   in summers past the peace
Was certain and contained.)

Maria Porges
Evanston Township High School
Evanstown, Illinois
1970

Robert Webb, Needham Broughton High School, Raleigh, N. C.

WARMTH OF GIRLS

there is silent goodness about in the eyes of warm girls.
i have known some; they appear in a sleepy night rain a
   night wind
     smiling inwardly to the purposes of their own comings
       and goings.

flashing waters and sunstreaming.

my summer is a gentle friend; her summer a soft-paw
   of the prowling death.
(to the disinterested: summer sprawls within itself —
   stretching, seeking a
      freedom for its own imprisoned leaves and
        grasses.)

a green god hugging the earth . . . !

she leaves in a mystery of time and smiles.
the last scene begins like this:
                "where burning sheaf of harvest
                brown stained November . . ."

Mitchell Hansen
St. Edward High School
Cleveland, Ohio
1970

Joe Tautimez, Gilbert (Ariz.) High School

QUOTRON TO IBM ELECTROLA

i   pron: the one speaking or writing
love   vb: to feel a passion, devotion
             or tenderness for
you   pron: the one being addressed
           BLEEP.

Steve Chase
George Churchill Junior High
Galesburg, Illinois
1970

SECTION THREE

Diane Woods, Whittier (Calif.) High School

43335

Across the table, on her arm,
The small blue numbers shout to me
Through the glass before my eyes;
And blue-gray hair winks in the cold
Yellow heat of a porcelain lamp.
She has long, angular hands,
With skin the color of filtered moonlight,
And a knotted, buried snake of vein,
Hidden in each wrist.
Around her neck, hung from a silver cord,
Is a dented yellow ring, twice as fat as her thumb,
That she slips aimlessly on and off her fingers
Her eyes are gentle and ageless,
But her nails are bitten to the quick.

Jonathan Rosenthal
Bronx High School of Science
New York, New York
1968

MORATORIUM

On Saturdays
We used to get up early
My brother John and me
To crawl like lizards down the stairs
And out the back door
To the barn
Where the creaking wagon sat
Among the rakes and forks
We used to pull the wagon
Up the hill
Along the dirt road
To the White's farm
Which was our first stop
We never missed a house
This side of the creek
At every door we'd ring
"Good morning"
Up bright and early boys? — Yes off
To an early start
Collecting paper and old magazines and
Telephone books
For President Roosevelt
And the war effort
And our boys in Europe
On some days it was bed springs
And tin cans.
There were bacon fat mornings
And liberty stamp drives.
We did our part.
And when at last we'd dragged
The wagon back
Over the last rut before the barn
We ran inside for lemonade
From a glass pitcher.

The war was won
And the boys came home from Europe,
Though some of them stayed.
We had done our part

That was during the war.
My kids used to ask, "What war?"
But now I'm in my easy chair
And my wife in the kitchen
Is serving hot chocolate in mugs
To hordes of sniffling kids
Blown in out of the cold
Rustling petitions and
Bristling buttons.
Last week it was
Leaflets and armbands.

My wife and I
We were in Washington
We had to go; it was
The least we could do.
The bus driver drove too slow
So we got there too late to
March. We stood in the crowd
And hopped from foot to foot on the frozen mall
And someone said "Hop for peace!"
Inside my gloves
I pulled my fingers from the glove fingers
To make a fist.
I wiped my lip with a fingerless finger.
We couldn't see the speakers' stage
Somewhere off in the wind.
The P. A. was speaking
Of the peace effort
And bringing the boys home.

In the kitchen
The kids are sipping and talking
Telling of adventures and encounters
With the great silent enemy.
Noses dripping, they hear of old ladies
Gawking and of
Curlered housewives calling them
Communists.
Fresh off the pavements
They count their prize,
The names they have collected
Like summer fireflies
In a jar.

But fireflies are elusive.
My brother John and me,
We used to chase them with tangled
Cheesecloth, on the warm August air.
And though we swam and jumped
For the orange fires, they dangled
Higher out of reach and left us standing there
Scanning the night
For more distant points of light.
Cheesecloth like bullets is as poor
A way to catch fireflies.
You have to cup them in your bare hands.

David Sack
George W. Hewlett High School
Hewlett, New York
1970

SLUMBER OF PROPHECY

Sleep comes to her
Encased in an infinity of lollipops and icecream cones
    of the mind
Unaware of the past, present, or doubtful future
    Sleep comes to her.

Let her sleep. Do not wake her.
One day she may have to know that all roses try to be red
That white and yellow blend into crimson
    on a far away, not so make-believe land
    Let her sleep.
Someday she may hate a man because his color is
  like that
    of her teddy-bear, nestled to her cheek
    Let her sleep
Until the others awake.

Stephen Kessler
Cedar Cliff High School
Camp Hill, Pennsylvania
1966

PRAYER

I raise my hands to you.
I will build a monument to you.
I will kill a goat.
I will kill a calf.
I will kill a man
Just to have one lightning quick glance at you.
I will kill a thousand men for you;
Just let me see you,
Just let me show the skeptic.
Please, please let me see you.

Kenneth Shorr
Royal Palm Elementary
Phoenix, Arizona
1966

Lynn Silverman, Reseda (Calif.) High School

FORTY-FIVE MINUTES TO SPEND WITH YOU BEFORE THE GALLOWS TODAY

I remember looking into your eyes.
I remember the rain falling.

> Rain, rain, falling down.
> Please, rain,
> Let me drown.

I remember smiling at the sunset.
I remember failing my mid-term health test.
I remember spying through the kaleidoscope.

> Now I lay me down to sleep; my bag of jelly-
>   beans at my feet.
> If I die before I wake, I leave them to my
>   cousin Blake.

I remember swinging a cat around by the tail.
I remember looking at "before" and "after" pictures
of girls in magazines and invariably deciding that the
"before" pictures looked better.

> Ha! Ha! She's funny!
> Calls me honey . . .
> Wants my money.

I remember trying to convince my parents that I still
believed in Santa Claus so I would receive a stocking
when I was thirteen.
I remember the bus screeching to a halt and the blood
flowing freely.

> Fire! Fire! False alarm!
> I fall onto my boyfriend's arm.

I remember feeding the squirrels in the park.
I remember the ambulances screaming louder than I.

> I say hi!
> You say 'bye!
> Hello! Hello?
> Goodbye! Hello!

I remember crying when my cat was killed.
I remember laughing when I saw an old lady slip on the ice.
I remember sucking my thumb because I thought that I would get beautiful hands if I did so.

> Jacky, Jacky, I've been thinkin'
> What in the world have you been drinkin'?

I remember crying when President Kennedy was assassinated.
I remember discovering there are no stars.
I remember stealing a box of chocolates and getting caught.

> To do it or not to do it —
> That *is* the question.

I remember wondering how it was possible for Jesus to sweat blood.
I remember the neon lights flashing eerily.
I remember giving up my subway seat to a Negro lady that didn't have a nose.

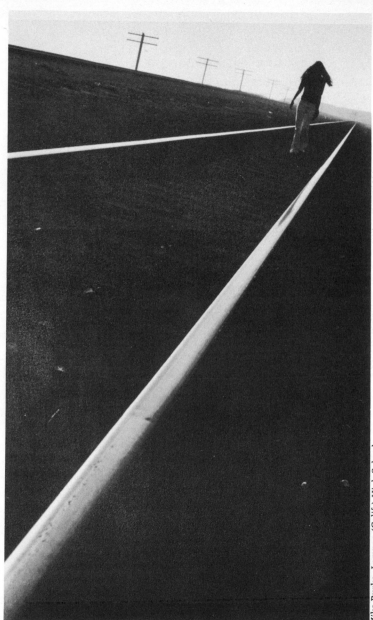

Mike Burke, Lompoc (Calif.) High School

If the train goes off the track
Do you want your money back?

I remember idolizing the Beatles.
I remember skipping classes so I wouldn't have to see
phony girls winking at phony boys.
I remember lining the inside of my dog's house with
my best friend's pictures.
I remember looking at false eyelashes and wondering
what had become of the people that had donated them.

You're darn tootin'
I'd like a fig Newton!

I remember winning a record from a radio station.
I remember squeezing your hand so tightly that I
knew it was possible for Jesus to sweat blood.
I remember wanting to curl up and die.

Georgie, Porgie,
Why did you have
To kiss the world
And make it cry???

Susan McLean
Hawkesbury District High
Hawkesbury, Ontario, Canada
1968

SECTION FOUR

Jay Waterman, Loara High School, Anaheim, Calif.

AUTUMN

Autumn is an old woman
      who is still beautiful because her bones are good
      who comes to breakfast in her diamonds
        and keeps the blinds drawn
      who comes to tea in yesterday's lace
        and uses the best china
      who comes to dine in apricot satin
        and eats walnuts
Autumn is an old woman
      who spends lavishly the heavy gold of the moon
      who has the plants in the conservatory
        painted sunset
      who lights a million candles on the gabled roof
        And never looks back to see them black

Ann Nelson
Highland High School
Salt Lake City, Utah
1966

42

RAIN

licorice-powdered cottage-cheese skies
unravel strands of rain
slapping and waffling water
to puddle punch the grass
into jabbed-out stripes

granules of sound
fluttering, tapping, unseen rain
plinking on sewer gratings and warm tar

steel splinters of rain
prickling and poking
flat turtleshell puddles
riveted by rain
throb into grass
escaping in rivulets
flee into sewers

Lynn Krabbe
Webster Grove High School
Webster Grove, Missouri
1969

MEMORIAL DAY

This soft, mortal rain,
    caught away by house gutters,
       lies like a mirror.

Philip Bowman
Apponequet Regional High School
East Freetown, Massachusetts
1966

43

WELL

There was a chuckle of frost
Lacing the brown edges of grass-blades
This morning, and its small bright teeth
Nipped our nerve endings, and snickered
Icily.

Little wet cat-paws
Made a perforated parade
From Juno's back-porch bedroom
To her flower-bed bathroom,
And stopped conspicuously . . .
And a summer-late robin
Shrieked desperately, "Fall is here! Fall is here!"

Diane Erb
Park Rapids High School
Park Rapids, Minnesota
1969

Robert Hathorn, Hardford High School, White River Junction, Vt.

IN THE WOODS

stepping carefully
      following a small path
         in the woods
      crunching the leaves
      collapsing small wooden
tents
      breaking into a flat plane
      little pockets of air

trodging
      is my new name for the tread
         steady walk

to the clearing
      in the pure places
      man has kept his business out of

to come upon
      the glowing circle
      in which
      i stand waiting for myself

           Ann Raphael
           Lourdesmont School
           Clarks Summit, Pennsylvania
           1969

MORNING SHADOWS

A cherry blossom,
Wet with dew, falls to the pond —
A sunfish rises.

AFTER A SPRING RAIN

How fresh a spring rain
Smells while walking barefoot through
Rows of sprouting corn.

Daniel Sell
Forsythe Junior High
Ann Arbor, Michigan
1968

Jeane Burton, Fayetteville-Manlius (N. Y.) High School

A PALE, FRAGILE ROSE

A pale, fragile rose
had fallen gingerly on
the demolished ground.

COLORED BUTTERFLIES

Colored butterflies
floating in the deep blue skies
smiling together

Judy Crusco
Nesaquake Junior High School
Smithtown, New York
1969

SPARROWS PLAYING

Sparrows, playing in
The sharp wind that blows the leaves
And turns the pumpkins.

ON MORNING SIDEWALKS

On morning sidewalks
Last night's rain recorded in
Pink earthworm cursive.

Bruce A. Byers
Los Alamos High School
Los Alamos, New Mexico
1969

Jim De Paoli, Our Lady of Victory, Cincinnati, O.

SECTION FIVE

BATHTUB POEM

Underwater
I rub my thumb along
My leg.   Bubbles,
Freed,
stream
upward
playing
ginger
ale.

Bubbles spangle
The water surface
Like welders' sparks.
The spangled water
Boils
And hisses.   Hisses.
Seethes.   Hisses.

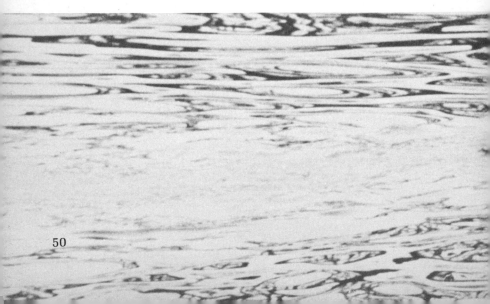

My thumb, working
Again, liberates, untethers
Bubbles.   They flee toward
Liquid rafters
Like
Convention balloons.

Grape-like
They cluster on
Every hair,
Ripening

Divers,
They depend on
The bathysphere of my thigh,
Till, mission complete
They resurface
In spirals without Bends

Randy Vander Mey
Central Christian High
Grand Rapids, Michigan
1970

John Engelman, Lakewood (Calif.) High School

DELIVERIES BPE

      Today i am
           delivering
Baby Penguin Eggs. ➞
          super expresso.
   themommyanddaddy don't
    expect me; i ran
        my first delivery —(with
unpenguined legs)
     An Egg cracks and
        a grōcker appears.
      raggedy ann smiles bloom
   because they
       have already
     four spinsels.
imusthurryfasterbecauseanotherEggis
     CR   ACK   ING
   (thank god for suction
     cup soles)
  another Baby added to Pengcare
     by the
Pishey Pamily
     (Penguins don't have good F'ers)
   Deliveries done
     leaving exhausted me
      i jump
through the next iceberg
       and
   scuba home.

Christine Bachen
La Sierra High School
Carmichael, California
1970

PERMA-PRESSED SHIRT COLLARS DON'T WILT; THEY JUST SOG

Sitting on a west Saint Louis fire escape
eating strawberries at night
and drinking water I can see
the couple on the second floor
watching air-conditioned TV.
There's an all-pervading hum
around me in the air,
not of locusts nor mosquitoes,
but Carrier and Frigidaire.

Old Man River he jes' keep rollin' along
occasionally turning up the body
of a 47-year-old business executive;
fell off the showboat and drowned (they say)
   how strange.

Next door there's a baby crying
almost 90 with the sun down.
Some one in the crooked asphalt
alley down below me
is leaving for a dance his
Mustang gliding underneath the street lamp.
From somewhere I hear the clinking
of some Saturday night bottles and
the sweat runs down my forehead as
I replace it with more ice water.

Charles Clifton
Ft. Collins High School
Ft. Collins, Colorado
1969

Bruce Berman, Palm Springs (Calif.) High School

CAR RHAPSODY

All night we steamed the windows
With wild laughter,
And raced our red-tailed comets
Up and down the avenues;
Streaked, pinwheel-eyed and chortling,
Transfixed in fiery lights,
Across mad glass-reflections
That warped us shallow,
And past the station
Along the tracks to open sky.
The wide absorbing dark
We shattered, living as if dawn
Would bring us death;
Sleep is for others;
We can always sleep
But never live again.

Barbara Subirge
Williston High School
Williston, North Dakota
1968

MY FAITHFUL HOSS, CLYDE

Fighting my way through the deep-woven pile
of the brown and green fragments of the rec-room rug,
dragging my dreams through a cloud of dust
billowing, pillowing, senselessly choked
by millions of planets, the whole universe of wind-driven
dust motes
slamming my tonsils, filling my lungs,
I slowly wake up from inopportune slumber,
narrowly catching the buffalo race.
Which actually wasn't a race at all,
more of a stampede, actually.
And I had just been subdivided, parcelled out in
fifteen quarters,
all the lots sold with waving pennants
by B and D Realty, K.C., Mo.
In other words, trampled by a buffalo herd,
I was left rather broken on the old open prairie,
with circling buzzards and faithful hoss Clyde,
all waiting patiently for me to die,
when one would leave me and the others would stay
to partake of the feast: but Clyde eats hay,
so he didn't.

Paul Fuchs
Precious Blood Seminary
Liberty, Missouri

RELATIVITY

women
  in shawls
    sit calendar clear
  on the stoop
    wrinkled
    laugh and sing
        old songs
        sitting
  in the old
              country
      the farmer speaks
        Polish
          look how beautifully
              he calls
                the pigs

Martin Kreiswirth
Thomas Jefferson High
Elizabeth, New Jersey
1966

56

SECTION SIX

IN-TRADE

Andrea always
Liked to share
So
When she died
We felt no guilt
At taking the flowers off her grave
And selling them from door to door
Until we had
Enough to buy
A fuzzy cocker pup.

> *Lola Sierra*
> Alverno Heights
> Sierra Madre, California
> 1969

Bob Charter, William N. Neff High School, La Mirada, Calif.

THE FUNERAL

PART I

so there we were
at Tex and Bogie's
and everybody was keeping their
cool
even the bereaved
and even though we
were there for a funeral
it was kinda nice seeing all
those people again
till Hazel came
and said it couldn't have
happened at a worse
time
well God Damn
what are we supposed to do
"a pardon me Hazel
I was wondering if
it's alright with you
if Johnny dies this week,
I mean if you're not busy
or something"
but we just love her to
come and tell us
all about her operation
and her daughter's divorce
and really cheer us up.

PART II

the shroud wasn't anywhere near the
deceased
it fell on us as the time got near
funny how a guy's name changes
as soon as he dies
no longer is he Johnny
or John
or Buster
or any of the names
he ever had
now he's the deceased
just that

Kevin Bales
Ponca City Senior High School
Ponca City, Oklahoma
1970

FUNERAL AT THE BEACH

What shall I do about the pale crab
    who clamped onto my finger with a single orange
      pincer,
    who died, as I yanked away,
    because the claw came off?
What can I do about the fear that hid behind
    bony eyes and glowed there like lumps of
    hot metal,
    as he scuttled frantically for the water he
    would never reach alive?
How can I explain, as he slowed and stopped
    on the wet sand, that
    he had caused me pain, and that I did not
    want to kill him, but yanked back involuntarily,
    in order to spare my finger?
Shall I recite to him the Laws of Priorities?
Or shall I merely toss his salty shell
    back into the water and
    watch him
    sink?

Edward Meyers
South Denver High
Denver, Colorado
1968

LEGACY

It is mahogany, china and roses
Resting in sunlight of warm afternoons
But the warmth is from inside, in rows of dark boxes

> Where silver from Florence
> Crystal of China

rest in their split shafts of shadow and light.

I lift the soft covers of dry, powdered satin
And spill out the silver, the crystal and wood
And kneel on the carpet with bright rings and brooches

> While fragrance of Florence
> Spices of China

Drift the sunlight like dust-motes of gold.

I sit in the brightness and tumble the jewels
Through hesitant fingers and small sunburnt hands
I slip on the bracelets, clasp on the pendants

> From far-distant Florence
> Strange-seeming China

And dream in the warmth of the late afternoon.

My grandfather gave me these shining bright treasures
The diadems, necklaces, rings — and the chest.
I dream of the shops and the small ragged street booths

Where he fingered the silver
Stroked the cold crystal

Sniffed the smooth cedar — and brought them to me.

A year and a day have gone by very slowly
Since the last treasure arrived cased in wood
and half a year since, wrapped in whitenesses,
   medicines,

      Killing the fragrance
      Scattering spices
He died in a cold afternoon without sun.

And afterwards, nurses, in stiff and pink faces
Opened the window and stripped off the bed

      Folding out fragrances
      Airing out spices

Cutting the last link to darkened bazaars.

And now he is gone. The silver lies dully
In its thick cover of velvety dust
The crystal is clouded with long-crumbled satin
      While fragrance of Florence
      Spices of China

Dissolve into nothing on warm afternoons.

Maria Porges
Evanston Township High
Evanston, Illinois
1968

WHEN GRANDFATHER DIED

When Grandfather died
Grandmother lay in her dank room
Wailing her blues
And watched the candle splatter its glass hood.

Red eyed and briar haired,
Her memory backfired,
She cried for bed and wedding picture
Lit by the burning wick.

We peeped to marvel at her,
Young with the power of wasting;
The candle fire of her years exploded,
And all the weathers of her life
Turned to blue-raging summer.

> *David Sachs*
> New Trier East High
> Winnetka, Illinois
> 1967

ANNOUNCEMENT

We are selling the two houses on the hill
and all the land on which they stand,
from Mrs. Johnston's place up to the daisied brook
where we went to fill kitchen pots
the summer the water main broke
and we brushed our teeth with ginger-ale.

We are selling the two white houses
which have rested dormant side by side
through a score of New England winters,
waiting for the snow to yawn
and rouse itself
and slide down the slope,
past Mrs. Cherinsky's Cottages, and Church Street,
down into the big ditch off the road
where we used to throw our apple cores
in summer, looking into the bowl of dandelion patches
and nameless purple flowers
and wondering with shivers of delight
if anyone would hear you calling
if you fell in.

We are selling our two houses
and taking one last look
across the road
at the crazy people in the gray castle-house
with the long-legged children who banged doors
and shouted in high-pitched voices,
constantly pounding the planks
of the sagging wood porch
against their bare, calloused feet,
coming and going at all hours
with a wild tangle of bicycles
and old Pontiacs and knee-high grass
in their driveway.

We are clearing out our things from
the white-enameled cabinet drawers;
and the red-faced grocer
will no longer fear
that we will come to demand
the choice pickle from the very bottom
of the barrel,
pushing up a sleeve
and plunging a hand all the way down
into the murky, liquid-green darkness
with seeds and peppers floating on the top,
then finding the right one
and getting it wrapped in white paper
and going outside on the hot sidewalk
to eat it in triumph,
the taste not half so fine
as the achievement.

Mr. Czymbalko, the dark, stooped farmer
whom I thought so lucky because
he could grow sweet corn and strawberries
and call it his livelihood,
will no longer sell us
berry-filled wooden boxes
and carrots with wet, black soil
still spotting the orange root,
and the lady in the bake-shop
who worked red-eyed one day
because of a death
during the night,
she will no longer set aside
a loaf for us every Friday morning
with a cake sometimes
or a box of sugar cookies.

We are selling the two houses on the hill
because pink-aproned Mrs. Johnston,
who used to give us

John Gale, Lyndon (Vt.) High School

peas-in-their-pods and pansies
from her little garden
is dying in a New England hospital
and because my sister has seen Europe
and my grandmother
the stark, white inside of an ambulance,
and because we can no longer
stay to watch
and make sure that the paint does not peel
or the shutters loosen
or that a congregation of garter snakes
does not make its nest
under our porch
as happened
one
July.

Nancy Sherman
Martin Van Buren High School
Queens Village, New York
1966

EPITAPH FOR A COMPOSER

I
am
not
sure
which
sounds
spoke
most
for
me

•

Edward Myers
South Denver High
Denver, Colorado
1968

John Pratt, Colonel White High School, Dayton, O.

THE GAMES PEOPLE PLAY

hit-skip
a game that people play
driving on the highway
looking for a vic-

timmy playing baseball
wind-up, pitch, long fly
he runs into the street
        that's all
we will go to his funer-

allen riding his bicycle
pedal, coast, pedal, coast
he sticks his arm out for a turn
        it's ripped off
by a great big sem-

irene is driving down the street
thickety-thump, thickety-thump
she's got a flat
a crowd gathers round
a car comes barrelling through
thud, thud, thud, thud, thud
        he mows them all down

Douglas Bugner
St. Wendelin High
Fostoria, Ohio
1969

SECTION SEVEN

JUST A GIRL FLOWERPRETTY

just a girl
    flowerpretty
  singing
     an
      old song
a cold song
  breathing
 the words
   slowly
skipping
   the
      rope
  double dutch
  she sings about
    summer
 the white
summer
    an old summer
  in an old song
  just a girl
       flowerpretty

Martin Kreiswirth
Thomas Jefferson High
Elizabeth, New Jersey
1966

Kenneth Shimizy, Pacific High School, San Bernadino, Calif.

Tom Schneider, Ann Arbor (Mich.) Pioneer High School

BRIAN SWANSON

One clean-sponge May
I cut a dead, damp cocoon
from a soft redwood fence
for Bad Brian Swanson,
who once beat up my brother
and threw a baseball
through Carlson's picture window.

Every time he sees me, Brian boasts cockily
that his parents are still paying for
the broken window; but, softer, almost shyly,
he always whispers that
the cocoon just hatched yesterday
and turned into a beautiful moth
with purple wings that shine in the dark.

David Thompson
Theodore Roosevelt High School
Minneapolis, Minnesota
1968

TO JULIAN BREAM

I have watched you play your lute
And bring the centuries back from invisible graves
   within us.
You sit alone on the stage
Pouring out your music that scatters
Like colored beads spilled to the floor.

You begin another piece:
The thoughts scurry down your nerves like
Excited squirrels on telephone wires
And release from your strong thick fingers
The sounds that are waiting to escape.

Edward Myers
South Denver High
Denver, Colorado
1968

Jill Fleischer, Killian Senior High School, Miami, Fla.

WATCHING MY GRANDMOTHER

Watching my grandmother undress is like a movie
because she is grey and white and silver-brown
flickering like film in the dark

her satin slip becomes as she bends
moving water and a cloud
hovers silver around her head

her lips are black and her eye sockets
are silent silent only a radio
tinkling like a real music box

Dianne Sisko
Philadelphia High School for Girls
Philadelphia, Pennsylvania
1968

Mark Alan Bretheim, Appleton (Wisc.) High School

WHILE SHE SLEPT

The curtains billowed.
    Balls of wind swept through, longing
        To touch her warm hair.

Philip Bowman
Apponequet Regional High School
East Freetown, Massachusetts
1966

Bill Austin, Simsbury (Conn.) High School

SUNDAY MORNING

A musty smell of
aged wood and echoing coughs
punctuate sermons.

Janet Montgomery
Riverside Polytechnic High
Riverside, California
1968

ELIS AHLQUIST

He crossed the sea when a baby
And married and missed the war
Missed being an artist and had children,
Rode through hard times on the back of a little store
Till his body peeled off and his soul found out
If it was nothing or not.

He didn't care for smiles
Or spreading grandfatherlyness. Behind doors
Was where he usually was, sitting at the piano in
    his room,
Hands on his knees and shoulder-deep in sunshine.

Meanwhile and since then his dreams knot in my
    brain too
His daughter's daughter, deep in different inches and
        minutes,
Let me epitaph him so:

> His imperfections
> Had their special shape.

> *Paula Speck*
> Bethesda-Chevy Chase High School
> Bethesda, Maryland
> 1968

PORTRAITS

I am not an artist because
Judy smokes Marlboros.
    She wears a cherry jumper and cherry shoes,
    a ghost sweater and ghost stockings
    And carries the box of Marlboros.
    Judy, lying on my bed,
    Spills blood and snow on my
    Raspberry and coconut spread
    Smoking.
    So I paint the picture
    And the critics say whatsa matter kid you don't
    got no
    Other crayon but red?

I am not an artist because
The queer boy has a fat neck.
    He wears the same shirt everyday on the bus.
    From the collar grows a neck
    Wider than his head.
    So I split the neck and head on paper
    And the experts say there ain't no one looks
    like that why
    dontcha draw flowers?

If Judy smoked Newports, the portrait
would have been balanced.
The heavy red and white would be
blown apart by a mentholated breath of color.
The critics would have said, "This carnival of
rainbows combines the double enjoyment of a
striking portrait and today's pop-art."

If the boy, instead of a fat neck,
had big round eyes, the portrait would be seen
as a charming face.
The experts would have said, "This visage expresses
whimsical, elf-like fantasy of a child
found in a young adult's face. His warm eyes
thrill us with a 'je ne sais quoi' sensation."

Janet Moshinsky
Philadelphia High School for Girls
Philadelphia, Pennsylvania
1968

Bruce Pratt, Fayetteville-Manlius (N. Y.) Senior High School

SECTION EIGHT

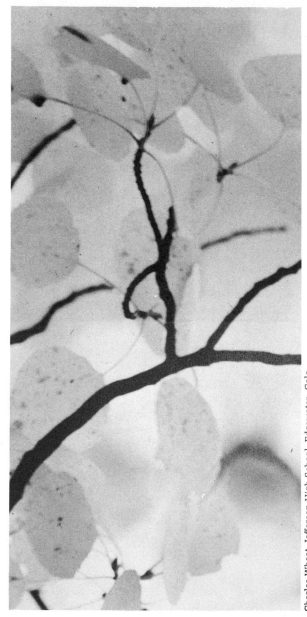

Charles Wheat, Jefferson High School, Edgewater, Colo.

LAWRENCE LOST HIS RING ROAD

I.

Lawrence leans from a polished window
shouting speed to the coachman.
One thin arm of maple sapling
slips along his finger,
springs the goldbound ring
from his fat red hand.
restive horses chop moss
creaking coach wheels;
shouts and a search.
one hand cannot hold alone
against a forest of fingers.

II.

between the rains the seasons
sunning like ringnecked snakes
bite their tails and moult.
the yellow ring rests
in a brown oak palm
aged in veins more in one summer
than any man's in seventy;
the leaf curls in upon its crumbling center.
sheep' sorrel and berry bushes, then pine
sprout in the wheelmarks of the road.
pale feelers, damp rootlets slip
around the ring bedded in black mould.
in their curling grasp,
the gold of Lawrence rests,
a foundation for empires
of wood and unraveling green.

Frederick Steinway
Phillips Exeter Academy
New York, New York
1969

THE INN

Mortared in an ancient time, stones,
    piled one atop another,
gather to a wall
      half-hidden by honeysuckle
           and laurel.
Above, the rough boards, pegged together,
    resist the creeping of vines, and the roof,
cluttered with wrinkled oak leaves,
          bends in the shadows.
Like a sun-speckled temple, worshipped and lost, this
  house:
    a place, with reminiscing willows
    that let   fall
streaks of light down on
      the brown-black rafters —
somewhere forgotten;
      here.

Couriers, leather-faced, hunched on
    iron-shod, brindled mounts,
stopped here on the road to Cumberland
because of the spring that bubbled
      in a mossed niche:
its waters ran unfettered across the dirt floor of the
  creamery,
    in the foundations of the house.
The mud-spattered horse would be led
      past the chickens to heavy-smelling
      stalls,
and a boy would toss June hay
    from a loft to the barking yard below.
And the man, with his wooden-heeled
    boots and long, stained coat, would
gulp a tankard of ale and a cut of mutton
      seared in the gargantuan fireplace,
and leave again for Cumberland.

Mark Daughhetee, Culver City (Calif.) High School

89

The road still labors up from the town's valley,
rutted when the mud dries and
      the dust rises to the over-hanging
    branches of
        maples and oaks alive
                with summer.
At dusk, now, a vixen slips through the
    brush, hunting, dark eyes
    flaring   if you cross her,
and she will pass on up near the house
and perhaps sniff at the flapping thin door.

Walnut beams —they built well —
    run solid as marble
to the roof of sagging pine shingles,
and the paste, mixed with
    sturdy water from the well,
      is dry lather between the rafters.
Hand-hewn, the planks have held
    through the winters,
        cold so that deer could not
        scratch out their moss,
          beneath the snows;
and the porch rests on its stones,
and by the door the wood is still
    splintered where yellow dogs,
    with flap-ears and thick tails,
    scratched for masters by the fire
        with the innkeeper's grog.

Fields, like ancient fields,
        flank the hillside; and linnets flap
    in the looming hulk of the barn,
its loft door, iron-hinged, swinging in the
        hazy sunlight.
Hay, unharvested since those days,
    since the days of the inn, stands tanned and lush,

Kenneth Valastro, George Washington Junior High School, Ridgewood, N. J.

Day Williams, Reno (Nev.) High School

mixed with dandelions and broom
and the thick-bladed grass of these mountains,
and nettles secret their old man's spittle,
staining the legs of those who pass.

Black eyes peer from black —
the black well has a keeper.
A mound of earth and half-circle of stones
lay the frog in shadow;
in ruined folds, he sits deep in slime:
a mute oracle.

A small pesky pup: he too with black eyes,
eyes searching,
and with a white blaze tufted on the brave chest:
he lunges through the grass, enjoying
the sun.
Was there a hound like this, racing and snipping
at the courier as he left the fire,
went to claim his mount?
And was there a frog for the dog to search out,
stare at with black eyes,
and ask the questions a dog would ask?
And did he, curved and shaggy tail wagging, follow,
as best he could, the reining horse,
and struggle through the brush and seedlings by
the road, the honeysuckle and laurel,
over the hill to Cumberland?

Jonathan M. Bowie
Woodrow Wilson High
Washington, D.C.
1969

TELEPHONE CONVERSATION

Half a mile of copper wire
separates us, yet brings us
this close
in protective anonymity
and privacy from each other
that eases our shyness
and fearful reserve.
But when I see you tomorrow
I know we'll regret
the impulse to confide.
Our faces will be closed
and our speech awkward,
but that will end in time.
The first time we talk this way
face to face
without fears of our vulnerability,
Then we'll have something
even more precious
than this first honest conversation
with the armour
of half a mile of copper wire
between us.

Susan Keady
Rutherford Junior High
Rutherford, New Jersey
1968

ALLIGATORS

Once, while waking from horrible
dreams
of slimy, green, and unsavory
alligators waiting under the bed,
I let out an ungodly scream
and scared the poor beasts half to death,
whereupon they slid and sidled away
to crawl under my brother's bed

and wait.

> *Jennifer Blatchley*
> New Trier East High
> Winnetka, Illinois
> 1967

Thomas Frei, North Haven (Conn.) High School

TWO DREAMS

I.

I was so small, and I lived in a dollhouse.
The plaster family of blonde dolls
Had inaccurate noses and blue eyes which would
not shut properly, and so at night
I had to cover their faces with rags,
so they could not stare me out of sleep,
grinning and grinning in their stiff chairs like thrones

II.

Be quiet. The five tigers
are asleep in the forest.
I watch from behind a tree
and do a fast mime of the ritual kill:
> Shake the spear
> Take aim
> Kill
> Skin the tiger.
I have not moved towards them,
and walk away wearing the skin cape
still dripping blood.

Martha Scheiner
Philadelphia High School for Girls
Philadelphia, Pennsylvania
1967

A POEM ABOUT THE GLORY OF THE FOOTBALL PASS

it's like see i'm
     standing in the middle of the street,
in california 68,
and i throw this long pass with my football
     and it's like perfect spiral down the middle
     of the street, it follows the white dotted
     line, and my brother catches it
on the run, and it's like
       in Yankee Stadium against the Packers,
and just now the street lights go on,
and a car turns the corner and heads for me.

         Steve Light
         Robert A. Milliken High School
         Long Beach, California
         1969

Carol Erikson, Reseda (Calif.) High School

Steve Tyson, Moorestown (N.J.) High School

FANTASY OF FLYING

He was so gross.   Folds choked fatly his necks and
            dripped
                    from
                          arms and thighs
        He said blinking piglike eyes darting,
                    I can fly
weightless I rise and waitless I exist
        time and space have no meaning   for the good
                    of all men on earth
I shall fly over the ocean to Vietnam
                    and set up a hospital on the 17th
                    parallel and care for the poor,
                    the suffering and all I need is a
                    little money
then he returned to the group and clanked away,
        for the chains that cursed him were linked
            coinsilver.

Irene Lindley
Roosevelt High School
Honolulu, Hawaii
1968

97

TRAVEL THROUGH THE
MIDWEST: WINTER

looking back on it, i guess the only things
                        out here
                                the same all year round
                    are the cows. having been here summer
                        and winter
            i know. they moan their songs just as mournfully
                        and twitch their tails just as
                                slowly in the cold
as they do in summer's drying heat. everything else is
    different
                    you don't want to climb the fences
                        the corn's gone out of the fields and
                            the ground
                looks like oatmeal when someone's poured just
                    a little milk
                                    on it
                and even the chew mail pouch tobacco barns

are a different color.
there are no barefoot sunbronzed girls and the trees
no longer have a shade to sit in.
ecclesiastes says that for everything there is a
season

this is a season for staying inside

an immense sadness hangs over us.
the only thing worse than green flatland is cold brown
flatland
desolate and dead.
it's depressing and it must bother even truck
drivers to travel under a sky gray
like cigarette smoke
on which someone's typewriter
left one last letter — the circling hawk.

Ron Meador
Burris High School
Muncie, Indiana
1969

99

SECTION NINE

PICKLE-THROWING

janet and i
        flirted with the guys down at
                mc   donald's
                a   half   hour
and they gave us a full cup of pickles.
we went out
        and threw them at convertibles
                bicycles
                lovers
and took an hour to decorate the mall.
and now today people are asking where
                the pickles
                came from.
they say the frat boys must have
                been drunk.

Kathy Swan
Mayo Senior High
Rochester, Minnesota
1967

YOUR RIVER KEEPS GETTING WIDER

I stood surrounded
by white sheets and long green grass
and a wind that possessed
a flair for moving the sun.

I couldn't help but
sit down and watch
the windmills, all different colors,
shaking hands like old
politicians.

But the sheets are blown away
now and the sun has faded, just
as the windmills have crumbled.
All the time I sat in the long
grass hiding, watching everything
change.
And it didn't make so much difference
about telling Sarah what to do;
she could've done without
me.

David Seppa
Cloquet High School
Cloquet, Minnesota
1968

Charles W. Fisher, Community High School, North Downers Grove, Ill.

THE SENTINEL

I have watched you as you slept
In the newest part of day;
I have knelt beside your bed,
Gently kissed you as you lay.

I have crept inside your door.
Sat, for hours, ever still,
Seen you slumber on in peace;
I have come and gone at will.

I have listened to you breathe
While the night became the dawn;
And as the shadows left the room
I have touched your face, and gone.

I have loved you for a time,
Have wished you were my own;
I have watched you as you slept —
You have never known.

Michele Watson
Washington-Lee High School
Arlington, Virginia
1967

EPITAPH T' THEM THAT'S GONE BEYOND

Johnny's jazz is on the Edison,
My feet are in my boots,
I sit here writing with a fine quill pen
Thinkin' about the girls I've met.
Many come and many go,
They mostly go,
Not to my surprise.
It comes to me as naturally . . .
As the fallin' rain to leaves.
I loved one once,
And she loved me,
Then along came Stan,
Like Getz on the record,
With a fine melodic line
Which took her while I was away.
I still think about that one
When I need someone to talk to, ya see
She understood the way I thought
And could travel the channels of my mind,
Like a gondolier in Venice.
I went away, mostly alone,
Traveled the waters up north.
I came back to a new dawn
With new teachers, not only the book kind,
But the kind that will teach ya
When you're out of your class,
Or that you're not the trite kind,
Or that she wants to be the boss.

Well, the latest has left
And I'm silent again
With nothing but what started it all,
The music and the drama,
The latter might leave without some help.
But what was it that Bob said?
O yea,
"When ya ain't got nothin,'
Ya got nothin' to lose."
That's it.

Dan Partner
Wheat Ridge High School
Wheat Ridge, Colorado
1966

Neill Collins, Reseda (Calif.) High School

YOU HITCH-HIKED

you hitch-hiked
   your way into my
    strictly conservative life
  and sprinkled a bit
    of wanderer's dust
that you brushed from
   your jacket
  into my heart
   and turned
     me against
  the established things

a little
   wanderer's lust
gripped my soul
   and unknowingly or
    maybe not
you swung a bit of love
   tied on a string
  before my eyes
  (like a tidbit before a dog)
   i brushed
  aside the people
who strove to restrain
   me
from snapping at the string

— just as
i readied myself
   to leap
you pulled the string away
   turned,
  and walked
   haughtily
towards the road again

Susan Keown, West Phoenix (Ariz.) High School

... now that i
        have regained
my fool's composure
        and have begged
                forgiveness
for my erotic behavior
        i scold
                myself
for being so very childish.
        but i still pick up
                hitch-hikers
knowing it's the
                only way
        i may ever
                see you again.

Gaylann Merzian
Evergreen Park High School
Evergreen Park, Illinois
1969

DUSK

A thin glass ball
floated down
through the clouds.
A vendor cried,

"Make the lady hap-pee!
Make the children hap-pee!
They are big;
They are beautiful."

I brought you a balloon.
I brought you flowers.

"Fresh out flowers —
Pompons, jonquils!
Fresh out flowers —
Jonquils, pompons!"

A jonquil, a pompon,
I offered you both
and a big balloon,
to sail away with,
into the night.

Mark Silk
Montclair High School
Montclair, New Jersey
1968

SECTION TEN

CROWS

Slowly at first
Spring
Seeps into the earth
And air, the first robin
Returns
And begins to sing in his
Tree, the sun
Props the grass
Up on its toes once more,
The earth
Puts out her yellow flags to talk
To the sun, and
Everyone is busy gossiping
About his winter vacation, when
Suddenly
The crows are back again! Can't spring
Ever shake
Those things out of her tail? —
Nature's black sheep
That nobody wants.

Paula DeMichele
Harbor High School
Ashtabula, Ohio
1967

THE LAKE

Some days the lake
Is just a
Lake, its waves
Flowing against the shore,
And the sun
Setting over it, casting from the horizon
To the shore a fire-pillar; but
Other days the lake
Is a ball of
Quicksilver
Shimmering in the
Cupped hands of the earth,
And the sun
Never even tries
To peek through the cracks
In the earth's fingers
At all.

Paula DeMichele
Harbor High School
Ashtabula, Ohio
1967

Keith Houlberg, Reseda (Calif.) High School

BEAR HUNTING SEASON IN PRICE COUNTY, WISCONSIN, 1968

Walking through a darkened woods
and ducking drifting clots of snow,
bending, scraping, branches shaking
burdened boughs onto my back,
powdering my shoulders with the snow
and straining through a woven tangle
of brown dark branches my face is struck
by the glare of moon on the shine of snow
on the darkened rows of the late-plowed field.
  And colors are never in the scene,
just tree-grey, moon-glow, black-gloom,
and a rich thick darkness of old earth and night-trees
and a heavy silver sky.
    And out in the center of the field,
piled high, seen through clouds of breath,
a mound of darkened shapes of matter,
dark and glinting and hung with mist,
seen only dimly in the moon-clear night,
a mound of dark against the black,
its shouldered silhouette mounting high
above the shadow of the woods,
into the subtly silvered sky
casting a shadow of its own,
stretching far on the furrowed field.
      And the sudden shape of night comes
        clean
as the eye adjusts to fantasy:
 a pile of bears, their lumbering grace
now finally stilled in the awful night;
shut eyes, closed ears, jaws loose with death,
their massive dark bulk marred here and there
by moistened glints on matted fur
and barely noticed shades of red.

The immensity of mountains,
dark snow-drifted hills,
all contained in a pyramid
on a snowy night, full moon.
Another night much later, on another winter moon,
the same field quiet and empty,
bars of jet stroke silver snow:
No mountain now, they're gone away,
no bones or hides or even imprint of weight
on the dark-plowed field.

Paul Fuchs
Precious Blood Seminary
Liberty, Missouri
1968

Kenneth Valestro, George Washington Junior High School, Ridgewood, N. J.

Dana Franklin, Muzzey Junior High School, Lexington, Mass.

WIND

Will-o'-the-wisp—fool's gold of the sky
lean and bittersweet
sunburnt and ice-tipped
The rope and saddle wind
The yesterday wind
big and proud
from the slabs of sun-silenced adobe
from the Wind Rivers
The spook wind

Ann Nelson
Highland High School
Salt Lake City, Utah
1966

116

ENDING

The sky is falling;
Blue pieces lie among the daisies.
If I pick one up
And hold it to my eye
The world is simple.

Stars sparkle in the grass
I'll twist one
In my hair, and
Run barefoot through
The scattered sky.

When the sun plummets down
Catch it for a
Yellow ball.
We'll arc it high
Where the sky once was.

Lyra Ward
Cass Technical High School
Detroit, Michigan
1967

R. Kevin Ryan, Peabody School, Cambridge, Mass.

117

SECTION ELEVEN

COLORS

Red is blood and death,
vivid nightmares and
brilliant fire. It's euphoria
and victory, psyche smashing,
kings and queens and worms.
Sherry-with-a-cherry and
gang fights in the black of
night and anger, and walking
into the girl's room if you're a boy.

Blue is a ghetto, run down tenement
shacks, men in pressed blue suits
ride in blue cars and have little cans
of mace and smash your head for no
reason. Blue is before the storm, the hot
part of the flame, a deserted room, the
dead bird in the yard. Blue is being
the last person on earth and no
telephone.

White is a Janus-faced color
being purity as well as KKK
hoods, peace but polluting soapsuds,
love but the front for premeditated
murder, white is calm, and white the
color of Alaskan white-outs. White
is dry wine, mothballs and sour
cream and the cloud of a nuclear
bomb.

James Newman
Muzzey Junior High
Lexington, Massachusetts
1969

Terrence Deters, Our Lady of Victory, Cincinnati, O.

AUNT SARAH DIED
ONE SUMMER NIGHT

Aunt Sarah died on a wicker chair on the porch one
      summer night with a cold lemonade and a Japanese
      fan and a dozen night bugs dancing around the 60
      watt bulb.

While the crickets chattered in the lawn,
      and the dog scratched and bit at his fur
      and the big black horsefly buzzed around the
      ceiling in our hot sticky kitchen.

While Mat and I kicked off our sneakers
      and ran over the wet grass, grabbing at the night
      for fireflies.

While Ma and Pa were driving to town
      in the green vegetable truck that smelt like
      tomatoes.

While Mary and her beau sat under the silver
      maple with leaves as big as hands, just watching the
      sky and saying nothing.

While the bullfrogs hidden in the cattails
      belched from swelling up with too much
      summer air.

Aunt Sarah died and the wind stroked her white curls,
and a thrush perched on the highest branch sang
her very favorite song, and the moon shone bright
so she wouldn't stumble going up the golden
stairs to heaven.

Lisa Hirschboeck
Dominican High School
Milwaukee, Wisconsin
1966

Stephen Schurrer, Alexander Hamilton High School, Los Angeles, Calif.

AFTER A DEATH

she forgot
    the sound
       of a
          smile

  and her eyes
faded
    like
  trees in an old
        photograph
  the hair-blown
    rain-fresh
look of her
    called
        the cries
    of a child in
       the night
and the
    soft of her name
  clicked tight
      until
    she laughed
      and remembered
        the good of him
      sitting in an
        all night movie
      the screen
        white as summer

Martin Kreiswirth
Thomas Jefferson High
Elizabeth, New Jersey
1966

FUTURE PROMISE

i lived one week on
a concrete beach where

a girl with winged-brown eyes
burned hairs from my left arm.

when i mentioned my intentions
of producing massive novels for art's sake she said:

"hitchhike far and long away, to a big city
like boston or maybe baltimore"

monday morning i shuffled off under a frosted sun;
for goodbye and thanxalot i stuffed a rose in each
    her ears.

tuesday night
i tripped onto the road;

a trucker killed me — he did not stop.
for goodbye he drove off flashing his brights twice.

once for each ear.

Mitchell Hansen
St. Edward High School
Cleveland, Ohio
1970

REQUIEM FOR AN OLD JEW

I could never tell exactly
what you were managing
among those body-robbed dresses and
"Rosa, dahling, have you heard?"
Those hangers mark a question in my mind.
But I noticed the certain way
the dresses swayed
               when you passed.

Then one day
In the fashion of their father
The boys held the

                    Annual Clearance Sale
And decided to finally liquidate
Certain portions of their own
               Old Stock.

You were sold cheap.

Today by now
Rosa has recovered
and resumed her proper station by the door.
Still, something more is less in those dresses.

               Dorothy Anderson
               East High School
               Salt Lake City, Utah
               1967

THE NORTONS

He always deferred to her —
It was always: "I'll ask my wife";
He never contradicted her —
But patiently said: "Of course."
He bore her scolding and intermittent nagging
With Stoic patience
And never let on to anyone how (or if) he felt.
And when he fell sick
In the winter that the Harrison bridge collapsed
Under Marty Krantz' cows
She was always there
with her grumpy ministrations
And a tongue sharper than ever,
Chastising him for the added trouble
She let him know he caused her.
He got worse (no wonder!)
And Dr. Ellis

Got him into the Vet's Hospital at Madison,
Fifty miles away,
And she could get up there to visit
Only once a week.
His health bloomed.
In two weeks he was healthier
Than he had been since his bachelor days;
He gained twelve pounds
Laughed,
And pinched the day nurse.
Dr. Wilson —
A young fellow but very pleasant;
Not high-toned or superior —
Promised him
That he could leave in the next week —
Monday next.
He sank steadily,
And died,
Late Sunday night,
Before she got up there to see him.
It was the only time he ever defied her;
She told him
To hurry and get well
And
To come home to her,
And
He died.

John G. White
Hononegah Community High School
Rockton, Illinois
1968

Bruce Berman, Palm Springs (Calif.) High School

TRAIN

The train,
minimized to some microscopic sliver of steel
spanning my 22 inch screen,
bears proof of physical censure
but refuses the burden
of conveying dreams to pine boxes.

Hundreds of thousands standing in stations
lay down their palms; the white,
the black, and gray flock
waiting in paths of a shepherd
and in huddles they murmur
"the train . . ."

Your wife, some tiny fragile doll
with unmoving face and arms limp at her sides,
is suddenly sucked up in a shroud of darkness;
the train screeches to a halt,
patient masses gathered on slopes near the track
are hoping the Gatekeeper was half so impressed.

Denise Zelany
Finney High School
Detroit, Michigan
1969

129

GREAT-GRANDMA WAITS

Great-Grandma sits in creaking rocker and
Waits. Little-seeing eyes, flapped by wrinkled
Lids in a face of yellowed parchment lose their
Sparkle with the fading of life's fire. The old
House is unpainted, the yard grows only crab grass
And dandelions, the weathered wooden porch sags
Under the drifting December snow. The housekeeper,
Retarded and slow-moving, sits in her room and
Watches T.V.; no one else takes so little pay to live
In a house of past dreams and death. No one is
There to cluck his tongue and shake his head. No
One cares. For Grandma is visited Sundays; some
Children live too close to find excuses for not coming.
But they stay only a moment's breath, and leave because
The house reeks of mustiness and medicine-smell.
Sometimes grandchildren and their children come on
Dull summer days when the swimming pool is
Closed; they shrink from age's wet-lipped kiss. And
Great-Grandma rocks away the shortening minutes
Of her day behind limp lace curtains, remembering
Past joys; wedding days, old songs, sons in tattered
Baby booties. She squints at the calendar, hanging
On the faded wallpaper walls of her empty world . . .
Only Monday . . . and she waits.

Diana Austen
Northwood High School
Silver Spring, Maryland
1966

John Kalil, Salpointe High School, Tucson, Ariz.

LAST WORDS

It seems today that no one cares
For really living. No one dares
To die before his time, though. No
One cares just when his time to go
Will be, or where it finds him. He
Just wants the action when it be.
He knows that death will strike or hit
Sometime when he least expe

Doyle McKey
Edna High School
Edna, Texas
1967

131

Tim Turqman, American Community School, Milan, Italy

SECTION TWELVE

James Rawlinson, Grosse Pointe (Mich.) North High School

BEACH

Big ladies jelly thighs
Parched lips and sand cookies

Mucous-wet sea babies
playing with a big ball.

White heat black feet
Dry rot why not?

Throw the ball my way
It slaps your plastic face

O mother the sky has me pinned
to the beach I'll never come home

> *Dianne Sisko*
> Philadelphia School for Girls
> Philadelphia, Pennsylvania
> **1968**

THE PIGEON

A pigeon landed wearily on my windowsill yesterday,
a cloud of feathers and dust,
a mass of flesh and bones.
He huddled himself and slept.
Framed by the rain and night,
His breast rose and fell softly,
One lame foot curled under him,
His feathers ragged from years of wind and snow.
As I watched, he woke, opening his eyes abruptly.
And there, in the depths of those black pools
Was the agonizing pain of flying for hours in the wind,
The clammy wetness of grass in the early park,
The bitter taste of the hard bread of the street,
The dulling agony of long winters.
So I opened the window to let him into the warm room
And he flew into the rain.

Jonathan Rosenthal
Bronx High School of Science
New York, New York
1968

N. Todd Peterson, Sunrise Park Junior High School. White Bear Lake. Minn.

SHEEP

Every morning I become a ram,
and after combing my short, stiff hair,
join the flock on the subway platform.
As the black dragon speeds into the station
we step back together.
(And I wonder . . . a forbidden moment;
the rushing sounds, the grinding
of the wheels over the hair of my body.)
But I must step back with the rest.

> From the subway window:
> the sun on the bridge burns with a living fire
> setting the morning sky aflame.
> And icy mountains on the river
> rush swiftly out to sea
> under the shining steel.

As the burst of momentary glory
fades behind the moving train,
the flock has settled down
to reading the grotesque advertisements.

This spring I will have my coat trimmed of its white hair,
in readiness for the warm season.

Jonathan Rosenthal
Bronx High School of Science
New York, New York
1968

RIDING IN

Riding in on
            great causeways
        borne on the
            breast of darkness
screaming
            down on wings
        of blackness
grey citymist stretching
                before
        gardens of sodium lights
swaying in
                tear-blurred eyesight
Coming in on
                a divine wind
        black rubber whirling
singing screaching
                    spinning
        heralds of death
at
        sixty-five miles
per hour
Swooping in
                dizzying monoxide
dreams
            clouds
                swirling upwards
great gasoline goddesses
        grasping the road between
their flabby thighs
                smiling crooked teeth
        at the night

Speeding
        onward
big huge memory cycle
hurtling forward
        memory passageway
cement roadway
looming larger and
        larger
    dreamtime reality
pressing farther
    desperation confirmed
  and
      disappears
a shadow
    into a shadow

Phillip Allen
Arvada Senior High School
Arvada, Colorado
1970

Bob MacKenzie, Lompoc (Calif.) High School

DISORDER

A pale moon ringed in white
    hanging antiseptically
        with shoulders hunched in the surrounding
          shadows

Waiting
While all space
    is slowly
       growing
         still

Suddenly the earth has stopped its motion and we
find ourselves suspended in the night like surprised stars

But the stars!
    They have become millions of tiny hands,
        beating their palms against the black clouds
And bewildered creation is shaken to its knees
in a hum of spinning ecstasy
And all mouths buzz with strange new speech

Carol Thomas
Tuscaloosa High School
Tuscaloosa, Alabama
1969

139

SOME UNTELEPHONED DIMES AND OTHER THINGS TO BELIEVE IN...

I. BANDAIDHOOD

the color of the sky was faded blue jeans
and it all came back to me in bounces off the roof ...
    somebody is crying because a cigar box full of crayon
        dreams melted in a patio sun
    and here comes a boy with his knees moonstained
        from backyard craters
    another is climbing over next to next door's fence
        into enemy laundry sheets
    while at the screen door a freckled force is mashed
        into tiny squares
    the others think him a wizard as he explains the
        theory of freezing koolaid into popsicles
but that was when today was only yesterday once
    and a thumb over a garden hose
        could make a rainbow halo in the sun
    when drainspouts would pour parachuted plastic
        men to the ground when it rained
    and it wasn't impossible to give names to all
        the bugs around a street lamp
        on a summer night.

II. AND THE WAY THE SHADE PLAYED IN HER HAIR...

the only once in a lifetime
after the flash bulb went off
I couldn't help bumping into you   so embarrassed
    I even asked if all pretty girls have sparkling specks
dancing around that makes them pretty
    glad you laughed   so relieved
    I even popped open four pop bottles

without thinking who would ever drink them
　　glad we sat　　　　　　　　　my crooked part and you
then we agreed people who made funny faces
would never have to grow up
and suddenly everything we had in common
went back to even the way the sun woke us up
static reflected in a spoon
I'm glad we decided
we'd talk better around a table then thick trees
　　even with straws in our mouths we could always nod
I told you to forget what time you had to catch
and asked if my chin needed a napkin
　　Outside was my favorite shade of outside
　　and we counted nice during the off hours
You asked if I dropped things in the dark on carpets
then I shrugged over
　　and you understood when you saw me draw a smile
　　on the bottom of my paper cup
You could have asked how much of my time was spent
pulling light switch cords or combing autumn waves
　　instead you listened to the way
　　I tugged the tablecloth

wish I could give you a name
you could wear like the time of day I wake up best

Phillip Parker, Central High School, Memphis, Tenn.

we can almost say each other's smiles anyway
    then maybe I could reach horizons
without finding gas stations or sunsets like dimes in a slot

I've practiced so now I can turn pages of magazines
without them sticking together
now my eyes are open and only movies blink
    and please don't pass me anything
    just touch me under the table
when you've seen enough of my stare
or think you should be home in time for

I hear a tear
the silence of your lips flowed like melted ice cream
into a molded frown   I couldn't understand
a stillness   like the runny nose I held during a supper
        prayer
        spilt jello from a plastic spoon
dropped erasers whose silent bounce left them a million
        desks away
        and bubbles I've blown
        that touched the sun
so please speak to me   again
so I can remember the life savers of your mint mind
        instead of my locker combination

III. A COCA-COLA REQUIEM

"if I can get the TV on in time I'll count how many
commercials it takes to make a night"

lonework   feeling sorry for the part of me
         that doesn't fit between notebook paper lines
guess the rest is in the margin for all to punch holes in

when someone answers, "Well, you know, and
   everything."
and you start to understand what everything is
you've noticed more than snow is clean away from tire
              tracks and sprinklers turn faster than
              autumn leaves

a school bus window   a stare through cold glass
thinking . . . there's a blur where there once was a ditch
but the sky is much clearer
    then the number of bullet holes in a road sign
feeling like every telephone pole passed
has tasted my initials at least once
    but the window has been bumping my temple
till it can see through me as well as I through it
    my first clear thought of the day

intermission   back already? your drink is fizzing.
did you find the man who opens and closes the curtains?
you're in love with him, you know.   did the cigarettes
   or words
you passed give you any ideas?   or did the people
   get in the way . . .

Howard A. Crouch, Jr.
Carmody Junior High
Littleton, Colorado
1969

143

Jon Lein, Fayetteville-Manlius (N. Y.) Senior School

SECTION THIRTEEN

IN DEFENSE OF CRAFTSMANSHIP

There is no such thing as a 2 a.m. poem.
Poetry's question doesn't settle itself down
like a fast flurry of blankets and flying feet
or turn off in mind like a lamp.
Poetry made in darkness ends up in noon
sooner or later, stumbling, squinting,
hiding its face and growling at the sun,
needing to be washed and brushed,
trimmed and polished, buttoned up and laced.
Only then can you send it off
to move along
in a world properly attired,
knowing enough of daytime
to handle business deals, go to luncheons,
chase taxis in the rain,
shake street-corner hands and smile,
take walks, endure, be examined
and all the time
explode
for being what it is.
                    But never
send a poem straight from its bed
and into the subway and the bus:
Curtain-crossed moonlight and a scrap of paper
will never get it through the day.

              Nancy Sherman
              Martin Van Buren High School
              Queens Village, New York
              1966

PORTRAIT

As a child she wore,
Unabashed,
Oversized dresses and coats
Bold black stockings and
Innocent white blouses that
Sagged, and reeked of cedar.
She wabbled around in Mother's heels
And had a special expression for each
Ill-fitting outfit:
Now a coy smile from behind a black veil,
Then a virginal blush from under Mom's
Battered white bonnet.
Her open child's spirit made
Either guise believable.
Everyone thought she was charming.
Now she walks quite surely, and
Never smiles a siren's smile,
And never blushes a virginal pink,
But wears expressions plucked
From somewhere in between,
And dresses in
Noncommittal gray.

Mary A. Boudreau
Philadelphia High School for Girls
Philadelphia, Pennsylvania
1967

SPINSTER POET

spinster poet, holy ghost of a library,
meager-framed,
hair and freckles brittle red,
color of old gildings,
she kept the wax of maidenhood
warmed by sly coquetry in her white crossed knees.

tinker in the art of shining fetters,
in the devotion of her craft
she died every day she lived.

light from passing faces,
sound of vines tapdancing on windows,
sparked friction in her brain;
under her hand they perished into pale verse.

David Sachs
New Trier East High
Winnetka, Illinois
1967

Steve Kurnit, East Meadow (N. Y.) High School

PORTRAIT OF THE POET'S WIFE

This woman
who washes a poet's socks
Stopped on her way
between the sound
and the song,
and plucked a beetle
from a motel rose.
Then, ignoring her husband,
She walked away and left the beetle
squirming and unrhymed on the ground.

Dorothy Anderson
East High School
Salt Lake City, Utah
1967

REHEARSAL FOR GOOD FRIDAY

All the trees waved
at three o'clock
and the people
looked up as they walked.
All the trees waved
like green torches.
A crazy breeze
feathered the tall fountain
in the circle.

We watched the
water fall and braid
the air. The day
felt like a fever,
hot and cool,
hot and cool.
We ran to the church.
Wet sheets of air
whipped at the closing door.
The sky was swelling
darker and darker,
and it would not rain.
The walls are nervous
with the chill stains
of perspiring lights.

Twenty boys
sit in twenty seats.
The green sky
wells and claws
against the
window glass.

The choirmaster stands
drawn black and tall.
He has walked
across the room
and bent
and slapped
the milky, knotting face
of Thomas Mott. And each
boy feels the giggles drop
like stones; and each
feels
the thistles bunch
and splay across his cheek,
and fingers comb
his flaming skin.

The dark room fills
with curling,
scudding words,
the hiss of cross
and Christ,
the soft stones
of love and shame
sinking through us
like slow, visceral winds.

And as he shouts,
and weeps,
his hands are fists,
nails wedged and white.
His hands are riding,
hitting air.

The words are far away.

   ****

The choirmaster stands before us,
his eyes shut,
hearing the chords
of his own dark love.

Veins lace his head.
Over the worn keys
his arms are out like planks.

David Suter
Bethesda-Chevy Chase High School
Bethesda, Maryland
1967

Peter Ballastine, Judson School, Scottsdale, Ariz.

SECTION FOURTEEN

M. Randall Oppenheimer, Birmingham High School, Van Nuys, Calif.

NINETY

I runs a meeyan miles a hour
through daylight
bowling over diamons
and just generally being a hazardous
animal

Bruce Graham
Edmonds High School
Edmonds, Washington
1969

THE TRAFFIC LIGHT

The traffic light,
Giddy with the height of power,
Swayed in careless stillness,
Switched from green to amber,
Then swift, to red,
As if to halt the wind.

Doyle McKey
Edna High School
Edna, Texas
1967

ONCE UPON

Asepsis
follows me kissing
who I do
wiping off the love I left
on lips

Bruce Graham
Edmonds High School
Edmonds, Washington
1969

BUT EVEN SO

You don't realize
that you run laughing, naked
through my mind
but you catch glimpses
of bare skin
in my eyes
and smile

Bruce Graham
Edmonds High School
Edmonds, Washington
1969

BECAUSE OF D

Why
Did you
come into my
life bright and burning
and then turn out
to be wax
like everyone
else?

Eileen McCormick
Rosati-Kain High
St. Louis, Missouri
1968

POET, MINSTREL

Poet, minstrel of moon-
stuffed metaphors,
your words

sputter from star-dregs
to periods. My words
on self-propelled

bicycles pass your flitting
chariots and periods
slide open.

Christina Starobin
Great Neck North Senior High
Great Neck, New York
1967

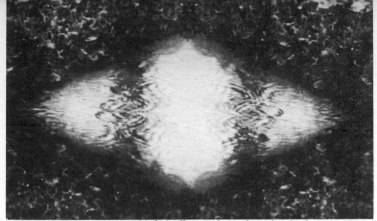

Linda Wallace, Palo Verde High School, Tucson, Ariz.

LOGIC

The Wind came and put
 wrinkles on the lake.
so I stayed (inside)
 because I didn't want to get
Old.

    Eileen McCormick
    Rosati-Kain High
    St. Louis, Missouri
    1968

COFFEE-POT

Our coffee-pot
used to sound
like doves almost sighing,
or maybe pigeons,
until we paid
to have it fixed.

    Gretchen Barrow
    John Burroughs
    St. Louis, Missouri
    1969

157

IN A DESERT GRAVEYARD

Heap a pile of bones and turn them all to stones;
Take one in each hand and smash them both to sand;
Mix the sand with blood and make it into mud;
Cast yourself a man and kill him if you can . . .

Edward Myers
South Denver High
Denver, Colorado
1968

ON WALKING TO SCHOOL DIFFERENT AND HEARING THE BIRDS

It was really kind of a screwy idea —
I mean out of my way like that;
But I'd worn a trench
Into every possible logical route
And couldn't see over the top.

David Thompson
Theodore Roosevelt High School
Minneapolis, Minnesota
1968

INDEX OF POEMS